JELLYBEAN'S CLOSET

BEVERLY STIFFLER SMITH
Illustrated by SHANA MORROW

ISBN: 978-1-64649-030-1

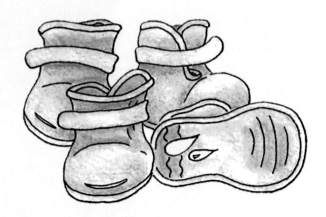

This book is dedicated to

all those who make or sell doggy apparel

and the fashionable fur babies out there

that strut their stuff with wagitude!

Jellybean is a little dog … with a BIG closet.

She has outfits for all kinds of weather.

One warm Sunday morning,
Jellybean looked in her closet.
"Hmm, what to wear, what to wear?"

"I see a dress that's perfect for me!"

One rainy Monday morning,
Jellybean looked in her closet.
"Hmm, what to wear, what to wear?"

"I see a raincoat that's perfect for me!"

One sunny Tuesday morning, Jellybean looked in her closet.

"Hmm, what to wear, what to wear?"

"I see a hat that's perfect for me!"

One cool Wednesday morning, Jellybean looked in her closet.

"Hmm, what to wear, what to wear?"

"I see a sweater that's perfect for me!"

One windy Thursday morning, Jellybean looked in her closet.
"Hmm, what to wear, what to wear?"

"I see a jacket that's perfect for me!"

One snowy Friday morning,
Jellybean looked in her closet.

"Hmm, what to wear, what to wear?"

"I see a snowsuit that's perfect for me!"

One cold Saturday night,
Jellybean looked in her closet.
"Hmm, what to wear, what to wear?"

"I see pajamas that are perfect for me!"

Jellybean is a little dog … with a BIG closet.

She has outfits for all kinds of weather.

She is one lucky dog!

About the author…..

Now retired, Beverly spent thirty-nine years as an educator. She holds a Bachelor's Degree in Elementary Education and a Master's Degree in Educational Leadership. Beverly learned early in her career that young children are drawn to the rhythms and patterns of language often found in picture books, which has led her to fulfill her dream of becoming a children's author! Beverly's puppy, Jellybean, has been the inspiration to make this dream a reality.

About the illustrator…

Shana Morrow has always been fascinated by art ever since she was a child. She says, "It's the thoughts, processes and modifications through which simple forms become beautiful works of art." Shana lives in south central Pennsylvania with her husband and son. Shana has a degree in Art Education and has taught in elementary schools and currently teaches in early childhood education. She is continuing her graduate education through Penn State University. Shana loves working with children and she greatly admires their expressive works of art and the pride they show in

their accomplishments. Shana hopes that her children's book illustrations will inspire young children to draw, color and illustrate their own stories.

About the puppy…..

Jellybean is a Shih Tzu/Bichon mix puppy, known as a Shichon. Jellybean found her forever home when she was only 14 weeks old. She loves to chase her tail, hide her treats, and take things that do not belong to her. She makes people laugh with her silly antics. She is a Therapy Dog with Keystone Pet Enhanced Therapy Services which means she is able to visit schools, nursing homes, participate in community events, etc., to provide comfort and sloppy kisses to those in need. She loves making people happy!

Made in the USA
Middletown, DE
28 September 2021